"Do I Look Funny to You?"

"Do I Look Funny to You?"

Written by Nicola Matthews
Illustrated by Eleanor Taylor

Hooked On Phonics®

Hooked On Phonics®

Contents

Special Words

Special words help make this story fun.
Your child may need help reading them.

giggle

principal

school

spider

teacher

1. Jazz Goes to School

Jazz, the space kid, and Zug, her space bug, are at Max's house. Max has to go to school, but Jazz does not know about school. Space kids do not go to school.

"But you must go to school!" says Mom. "All kids on this planet need to go to school."

"OK," says Jazz. "I will go to Max's school."

Jazz likes to do new things.
That's what space kids do.
"Come, Zug! Let's go to school
with Max and his dog, Polly."

Max giggles. "No, Jazz," he says. "Pets do not go to school. But let's ask Mom if they can come this time."

coochycoochy coo

Max's idea

Max's pals will like seeing
Jazz and Zug—they do not get to
play with space kids and bugs
all the time!

Mom does not like this plan.
"No," she says, "they do not let
pets in. Max's teacher will not
want a space bug in her class."
Max and Jazz know that Zug
is an odd pet. Space kids are

different too, but Jazz has good
manners—not like space bugs.
It's time to go, but Jazz can't find
Zug. She picks up her space bag
and goes off to school with Max.

On the way to school they see Beth.

"Where is Zug?" says Beth.

"Zug is at Max's house," says Jazz. "I am going to school with Max."

Then Beth sees Zug looking out of Jazz's bag.

Beth begins to giggle. "See you!" she says and runs off.

"Did I say something funny?" asks Jazz.

Max says, "It's OK, Jazz. Beth giggles a lot."

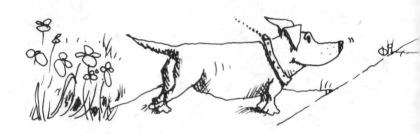

Next they see Fred and Tom.
"Where is Zug?" asks Tom.
"Jazz, are you coming to school?"
"Yes, I am," Jazz says, "but Zug
is at Max's house."

Then Tom sees Zug.

Tom and Fred begin to giggle.

"See you!" they say and run off.

"Do I look funny to you?" asks Jazz. Max looks at Jazz's six hands and her green fuzz and the three red feelers on top of her head.

"No," he says. "Fred and Tom
are just like that."

Just as they get to school
they see Jan and Pam.

"I am going to school with Max," says Jazz. "But it's OK. Zug is back at the house."

"Oh, no! He...," Jan begins to say. But then the bell rings, and they all rush into school.

2. Look Who Is Here!

Max's teacher is Miss Black. She did not know a space kid would be in her class. This does not happen all the time! She rushes off to tell the principal about it.

Jazz tells the children about her spaceship and the planets she goes to. But, one by one, they stop

looking at Jazz and begin to look
at her bag. Her space bag is
hopping up and down.

Then it begins to sing.

"Zug! Is that you?" says Jazz,
and she looks in the bag.

Zug is grinning his big space
bug grin!

"This is fun!" says Zug.

"Oh, Zug! You must not come to school. You have to go back to be with Polly!" says Jazz.

"I am!" says Zug.

"Woof!" says Polly, as she jumps
out of the space bag.

The bag is much bigger inside
than it looks!

"Oh, no!" says Jazz.

"Oh, yes!" says Zug.

The children think this is fun!

They all play and run after Zug
and Polly. But not Max and Jazz.
They know what will happen.

Polly and the children jump over the desks. Polly runs under the desks, and the children run after her. Zug zips all over the class. Polly yaps, Zug sings, and the children yell. It's lots of fun until Miss Black comes back with the principal.

"Sit down NOW!" says the principal.

The children all stop, and Polly runs under the teacher's desk.

Then Miss Black sees Zug. She gets very green and her eyes get very big and her chin drops.

"A spider!" she says softly and drops with a thud.

3. I Am Not a Spider!

The principal and Fred and Jan
bring Miss Black a drink. She is
OK, but she can't stand spiders.

Zug is very upset. He is NOT a spider. He is a space bug.

He does not understand why people do not like him. He is just a bug who likes to have fun.

The children are very good now.
They do not want the principal to
come back.

"Jazz, will you tell us about
space and Zug?" says Max.

38

"Well," says Jazz, "you need a pet in space. There is no one to play with. My mom got Zug to be my pal when he was still an egg.

"When he was an egg, I had to put him in a jam jar. When he hatched out of the egg, he was very small. Then he got very big. Zug can be good if he can have fun. When we are in space, he plays with the space frogs and space slugs. He likes to eat a lot," says Jazz.

"He likes jam and trash best.
He likes to sing space bug songs,

but they are songs that only
space bugs like. He is not a
spider," says Jazz.

"He has fun playing with the
wool and then getting all twisted
up in it. He likes to get wet,

but he does not like baths. I have
to grab him to polish his wings
and wax his legs," Jazz says.

"He does not nap much. But when he does, he naps on his back. He's the best pet a space kid ever had!"

Then Jazz gets Zug out from
under the desk and hugs him. All
the children clap.

"Woof!" says Polly from under the desk.

"Oh, OK," says Max. "You are a fun pet too!"

4. What About Polly?

When Miss Black gets back to
the class, all the children are
telling about their pets. They are
all very good.

Jan is telling Jazz and the rest of the class about what a good pet her cat Fluff is. Polly jumps out from under the desk, yapping.

She does not think Fluff is a
good pet at all.

Miss Black sends Max and Polly
out of the class.

Max is very upset. What will
Mom say?
When Jan tells the class about

her pet frog, Zug jumps up
buzzing! He likes frogs! They are
his pets too!

Miss Black tells Jazz and Zug to go out of the class too.

"I am sorry," says Zug. "I did not want to make you jump."

Miss Black did not think she
would ever see a bug with good
manners. That's when Zug kisses
Miss Black's hand! All the
children are still.

Will Miss Black pass out again?
She looks a bit wobbly. She looks
as if she is going to tip over—but
no, she hugs Zug.

But outside of class, Max begins to sob. Polly licks his hand to make him better.

Just then Mom comes to school with Max's PE bag. She sees Max sitting there and runs to find out what is the matter.

"Mom—I am sorry but Zug and Polly got into school. They hid in Jazz's space bag. They had fun, and the teacher sent us outside," says Max.

"It's OK, Max," says Mom. "I will tell your teacher what happened. We can fix this."

When Mom gets into the class, Zug and Jazz are telling Miss Black and the class how to talk like space bugs talk at home.

They are all sitting like space bugs
and acting as if they had wings!

Miss Black sees Max's mom and says, "I'm sorry, I forgot Max was out there!

"We are having so much fun! Max must come back in and bring Polly too. Come and have fun with us!"

And that's just what they did.